Everything's Gro...

by Niki Davies

Section One:
Songs To Sing!

Mummy's Tummy's Growing	3
Grandad's Whiskers	6
Each Little Blade Of Grass	9
The Balloon Is Getting Bigger	13
Daddy's In The Garden	16
Little Shadow (Echo Song)	19
Mister Sunflower	22
Duckling, Duckling, You Will Grow	25
Thunder Storm	28
Two Birds, Singing A Song For Me	31
Yellow Daffodils	34
Tiny Little Fingernails	37

Section Two:
Musical Activities 40
Music & Movement 43
Curriculum Linked Activities 44

Section Three:
A Musical Episode - The Window Sill 45
CD Track Listing 48

Series Editor: Sadie Cook
Music and text processed by Global Music Solutions, Surrey SM6 9BT
Cover design by xheight design limited
Vocals on recording by Niki Davies
All recordings orchestrated and engineered by Dave Corbett
Published 1998

INTRODUCTION

This book aims to provide simple musical material for pre-school children and Key Stage One pupils. The songs, actions, music & movement activities and performance ideas all combine to create a stimulating musical environment, which helps to cultivate and nurture enthusiasm for music in the very young. At the same time, the material is thoughtfully designed to gently stretch and improve the children's musical ability and build confidence in their use of language skills, body co-ordination, social development and awareness. The material is suitable for both non-specialist and music specialist teachers with the inclusion of backing tracks on the enclosed CD and easy piano arrangements in the book.

Section One: Songs To Sing!

The twelve songs which make up this section of the book all draw on the every day experiences of three to six year olds providing a steady learning process to help contribute to their development and knowledge. There are actions to accompany the songs, along with full versions and backing tracks on the enclosed CD. Through learning and singing these songs the children will experience an instant sense of achievement and pleasure.

Section Two: Musical Activities, Music & Movement and Curriculum Linked Activities

This section develops further the children's concentration and listening skills by exploring sounds through the use of musical instruments and by relating sounds to images and movement. There are opportunities and suggestions for the children to create their own musical instruments and to experience making music with these as a group.

The seven music & movement exercises use the excerpts on the enclosed CD as descriptive music for the children to act and mime to. As with other activities in the book you may only wish to use one or two of these excerpts, or prefer to dip into them over a term's work.

Section Three: A Musical Episode - The Window Sill

This short, easily producable musical combines some of the songs covered in section one with a simple script. The material is flexible enough to be adapted into an elaborate performance or to be kept as simple as you like. The children are able to develop more confidence in their musical and creative ability through taking part in role-play and performing their work to their mums and dads.

Whether used as an occasional resource or as a theme on which to base a term's work, the teaching ideas and activities in this book are designed to a clear, yet flexible pattern which is completely usable by musicians and non-musicians alike.

Mummy's Tummy's Growing

Words and Music by
Niki Davies

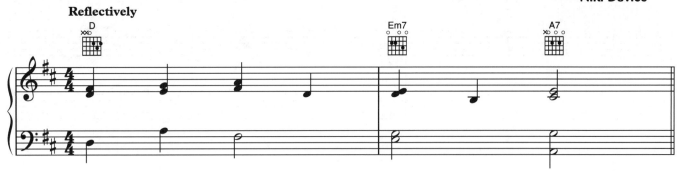

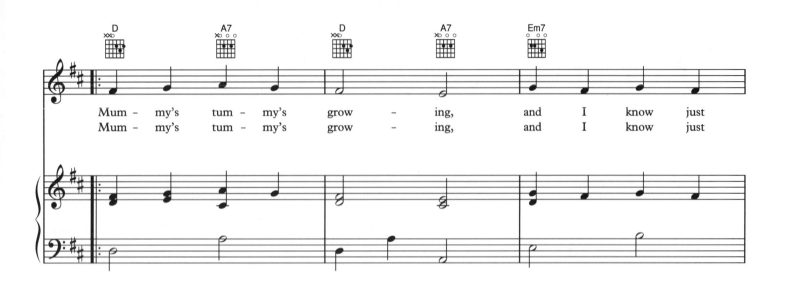

Mum - my's tum - my's grow - ing, and I know just
Mum - my's tum - my's grow - ing, and I know just

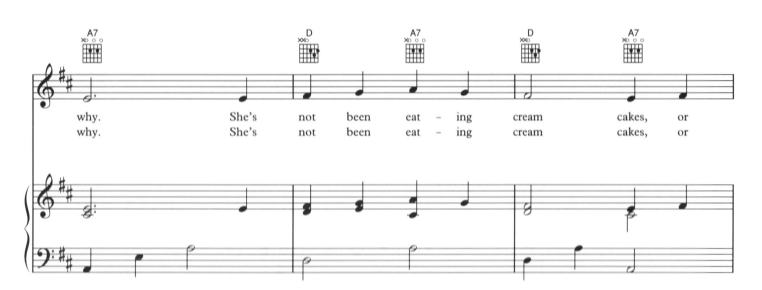

why. She's not been eat - ing cream cakes, or
why. She's not been eat - ing cream cakes, or

1. Mummy's tummy's growing
   And I know just why
   She's not been eating cream cakes
   Or too much apple pie
   She's going to have a baby
   It's going to be quite soon
   I wanted a new teddy
   But I suppose a baby will do

2. Mummy's tummy's growing
   And I know just why
   She's not been eating cream cakes
   Or too much apple pie
   I'm getting quite excited now
   Because he'll soon be here
   I think I'll ask my mummy
   If we can have a baby each year

Actions

Mummy's tummy's growing	-	Mime a big tummy
And I know just why	-	Nod head slowly
She's not been eating cream cakes *Or too much apple pie*	} }	Hold out arm and wave index finger from side to side
She's going to have a baby *It's going to be quite soon*	} }	Pretend to cradle a baby in your arms
I suppose a baby will do	-	Hold out hands and arms from elbows

Use the same actions as above for the second verse changing the last line as below:

If we can have a baby each year	-	Place hands together pleadingly

Grandad's Whiskers

Words and Music by
Niki Davies

With humour

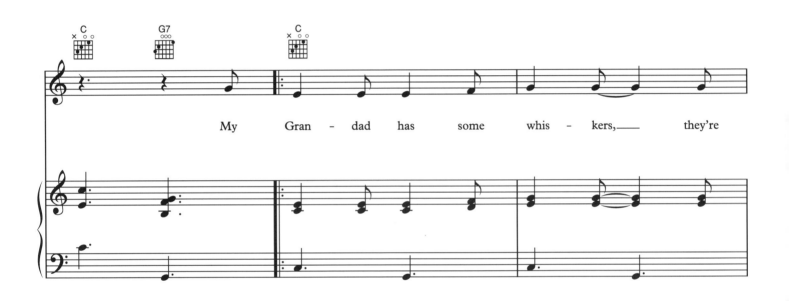

My Gran - dad has some whis - kers,—— they're

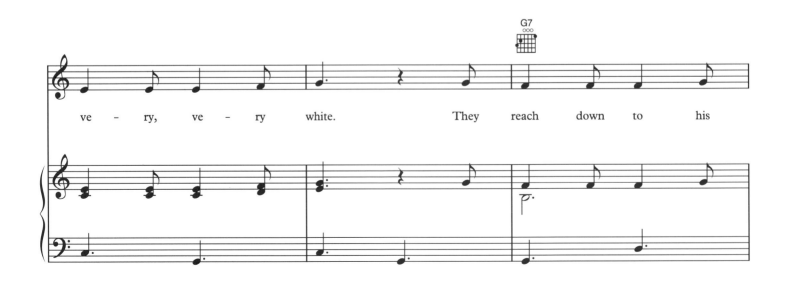

ve - ry, ve - ry white. They reach down to his

My Grandad has some whiskers
They're very, very white
They reach down to his tummy
They're such a funny sight
They're getting longer every day
He really doesn't care
A-CHOO!
They fly up in the air

Actions

My Grandad has some whiskers *They're very very white*	} }	Point to chin
They reach down to his tummy *They're such a funny sight*	} }	Point to tummy
They're getting longer every day *He really doesn't care*	} }	Move fingers from chin down to waist
A-CHOO!	-	Hold hands on either side of mouth like a megaphone
They fly up in the air	-	Throw hand and arms into the air

Each Little Blade Of Grass

Words and Music by
Niki Davies

1. Each little blade of grass grows quickly
   Each little blade of grass grows quickly
   When it's summer time
   When it's summer time
   Each little blade of grass grows quickly

2. Each little blade of grass grows slowly
   Each little blade of grass grows slowly
   When it's winter time
   When it's winter time
   Each little blade of grass grows slowly

Actions

Verse 1

Each little blade of grass grows quickly	-	Wiggle finger quickly whilst moving it upwards
When it's summer time	-	Wave hand in front of face (in a fanning action)

Verse 2

Each little blade of grass grows slowly	-	Wiggle finger slowly whilst moving it upwards
When it's winter time	-	Wrap arms around body

Balloon

**Words and Music by
Niki Davies**

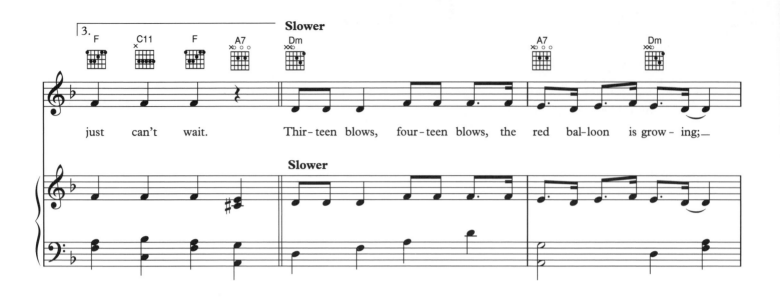

just can't wait. Thir-teen blows, four-teen blows, the red bal-loon is grow-ing;—

Fif-teen blows, six-teen blows, the red bal-loon is grow-ing.— Sev-en-teen, eight-een,

nine-teen, Bang!! Oh, now I'm back to where I be-gan!

1. One blow, two blows
    The red balloon is growing
    Three blows, four blows
    The red balloon is growing
    How many puffs will it take?
    The balloon is getting bigger
    And I just can't wait

2. Five blows, six blows
    The red balloon is growing
    Seven blows, eight blows
    The red balloon is growing
    How many puffs will it take?
    The balloon is getting bigger
    And I just can't wait

3. Nine blows, ten blows
    The red balloon is growing
    Eleven blows, twelve blows
    The red balloon is growing
    How many puffs will it take?
    The balloon is getting bigger
    And I just can't wait

4. Thirteen blows, fourteen blows
    The red balloon is growing
    Fifteen blows, sixteen blows
    The red balloon is growing
    Seventeen, eighteen, nineteen,
    BANG!!
    Oh, now I'm back to where I began!

Actions

One blow, two blows	-	Make 'megaphone' hands on each side of mouth, moving body slightly forward for each blow. Use this action throughout for the counted blows.
The red balloon is growing	-	Draw a circle in the air
The balloon is getting bigger *And I just can't wait*	} }	Move hands and arms wider and wider
BANG!!	-	Clap hands together loudly
Oh, now I'm back to where I began!	-	Place hands on waist and look disgruntled

Daddy's In The Garden

Words and Music by
Niki Davies

Lyrics:

Dad-dy's in the gar-den, Dad-dy's in the gar-den,

Dad-dy's in the gar-den plant-ing seeds.

He tried to grow some car-rots but
He tried to grow some cab-ba-ges but
He tried to grow some let-tu-ces but

they ne-ver came, so Dad-dy shout-ed both-er! And had to start a-gain.
they ne-ver came, so Dad-dy shout-ed both-er! And had to start a-gain.
they ne-ver came, so Dad-dy shout-ed both-er! And

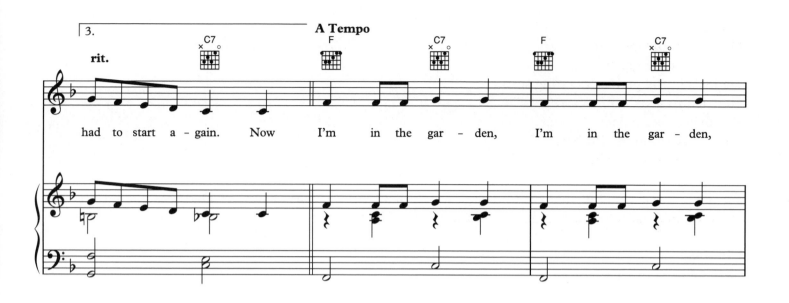

had to start a - gain. Now I'm in the gar - den, I'm in the gar - den,

I'm in the gar - den plant - ing seeds. My gar - den's grow - ing well, I

think you will a - gree. So next time Dad - dy, leave it to me!

Verse 1
Daddy's in the garden
Daddy's in the garden
Daddy's in the garden planting seeds
He tried to grow some carrots
But they never came
So Daddy shouted "Bother!"
And had to start again

Further verses: Ask the children to decide which plants, vegetables or flowers Daddy is going to try and grow, eg cabbages, lettuces, radishes, and use these for more verses.

Final verse
Now - I'm in the garden
I'm in the garden
I'm in the garden planting seeds
My garden's growing well
I think you will agree
So next time Daddy
Leave it to me!

Actions

Verse 1

Daddy's in the garden	-	Point finger (to the garden)
Planting seeds	-	Pretend to plant seeds in the ground
They never came	-	Hold out hands and arms from elbows
Daddy shouted "Bother!"	-	Place hands on waist

Final Verse

I'm in the garden *Planting seeds*	} }	Pretend to plant seeds
My garden's growing well *I think you will agree*	} }	Raise hands from waist up above head
So next time Daddy, leave it to	-	Place hands on waist
Me!	-	Point to self

Little Shadow (Echo Song)

Words and Music by
Niki Davies

1. Follow me (follow me)
    Little shadow (little shadow)
    Follow me (follow me)
    All day long (all day long)

2. Sometimes you are very small
    Then you're hardly there at all
    Then you start to grow and grow
    You really are a so and so

3. Run with me (run with me)
    Little shadow (little shadow)
    Skip with me (skip with me)
    All day long (all day long)

4. I can't run away from you
    You're always at my side
    But when it's grey and cloudy
    You run away and hide

Actions

Follow me	-	Use hand or finger in a beckoning action
Sometimes you are very small	-	circle hands close together
Then you're hardly there at all	-	Hold index finger and thumb close together
Then you start to grow and grow	-	Raise both arms up
Run with me	-	Use hands to create a running action
You're always at my side	-	Point to side of body
When it's grey and cloudy	-	Point to the sky
You run away and hide	-	Rest side of head on both hands in a 'sleepy' position

Mister Sunflower

Words and Music by
Niki Davies

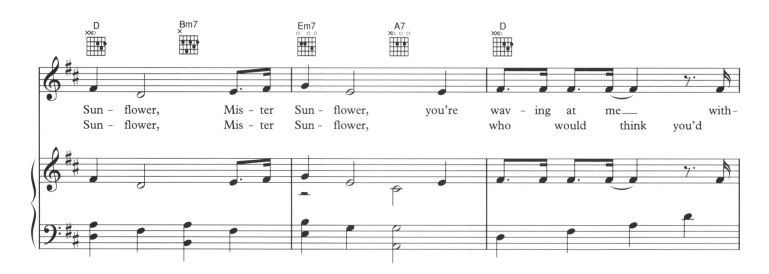

-out a sound. You're sway-ing in the breeze,_ you're
grow so tall.__

laugh-ing at the trees.__ You're hap-py__ as a sun-flower could

be.   Mis-ter be.

1. Mister Sunflower, Mister Sunflower
   Your face is golden and round
   Mister Sunflower, Mister Sunflower
   You're waving at me without a sound
   You're swaying in the breeze
   You're laughing at the trees
   You're happy as a sunflower could be

2. Mister Sunflower, Mister Sunflower
   You were a seed so small
   Mister sunflower, Mister Sunflower
   Who would think you'd grow so tall?
   You're swaying in the breeze
   You're laughing at the trees
   You're happy as a sunflower could be

Actions

Verse 1

Your face is golden and round	-	Draw a circle with hands
You're waving at me	-	Wave hand
Without a sound	-	Place finger on lips
You're swaying in the breeze	-	Sway from side to side
You're laughing at the trees	-	Throw hands into the air from the elbows

Verse 2

You were a seed so small	-	Hold out a cupped hand
Who would think you'd grow so tall?	-	Hold hand as high as possible above head
You're swaying in the breeze	-	Sway from side to side
You're laughing at the trees	-	Throw hands into the air from the elbows

Duckling, Duckling, You Will Grow

Words and Music by
Niki Davies

1. Duckling, duckling, you will grow
   Duckling, duckling, this I know
   You'll be a duck and I'm not wrong
   With a quack, quack, quack
   It won't take long

2. Puppy, puppy, you will grow
   Puppy, puppy, this I know
   You'll be a dog and I'm not wrong
   With a woof, woof, woof
   It won't take long

3. Kitten, kitten, you will grow
   Kitten, kitten, this I know
   You'll be a cat and I'm not wrong
   With a meow, meow, meow
   It won't take long

4. Piglet, piglet, you will grow
   Piglet, piglet, this I know
   You'll be a pig and I'm not wrong
   With an oink, oink, oink
   It won't take long

5. Chick, chick, you will grow
   Chick, chick, this I know
   You'll be a chicken and I'm not wrong
   With an cluck, cluck, cluck
   It won't take long

Actions

Duckling, duckling (or whichever animal)	-	Hold arms out in front with hands together
You will grow	-	Move arms outwards
I'm not wrong	-	Point to self
Quack, quack, quack	-	Open and close fingers like a duck's beak
Woof, woof, woof	-	Nod head with each 'woof'
Meow, meow, meow	-	Curl hands over and hold next to face like a cat's paws
Oink, oink, oink	-	Nod head with each 'oink'
Cluck, cluck, cluck	-	Move elbows in and out from the waist
It won't take long	-	wave index finger from side to side

Thunder Storm

Words and Music by
Niki Davies

Expectantly, at a moderate speed

The clouds are grow - ing

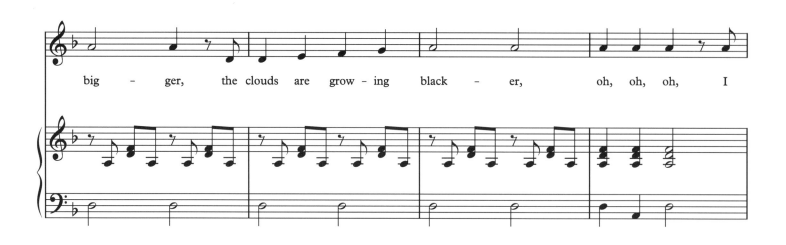

big - ger, the clouds are grow - ing black - er, oh, oh, oh, I

think there's going to be a thun - der storm.
The

The clouds are growing bigger
The clouds are growing blacker
Oh, oh, oh
I think there's going to be a thunder storm
Flash goes the lightning
Crash goes the thunder
FLASH! CRASH!
What a thunder storm

Actions

The clouds are growing bigger	-	Open arms wide
The clouds are growing blacker	-	Open arms wide again
Oh, oh, oh *I think there's going to be a thunder storm*	} }	Place hands flat on sides of face
FLASH! CRASH!	-	Clap once on each word

As suggested in the music, the children could also use percussion instruments for the clashing thunder and lightning.

Two Birds,
Singing A Song For Me

Words and Music by
Niki Davies

1. Two birds, two birds, singing a song for me
   Two birds, two birds, singing a song for me
   I can see the dawn is breaking
   What a lovely sound they are making
   Two birds, two birds, singing a song for me

2. Four birds, four birds, singing a song for me
   Four birds, four birds, singing a song for me
   I can see the dawn is breaking
   What a lovely sound they are making
   Four birds, four birds, singing a song for me

3: Six birds ... etc

4: Eight birds ... etc

5: Ten birds ... etc

Actions

Two birds	-	Hold out two fingers (for the following verses hold out the appropriate number of fingers)
I can see the dawn is breaking	-	Hold flat hand above forehead, as if looking
What a lovely sound they are making	-	Hold flat hand behind ear, as if listening

Yellow Daffodils

Words and Music by
Niki Davies

Moderately, with a swaying feel

Yel - low daf - fo - dils, yel - low daf - fo - dils,
Blue for - get - me - nots, blue for - get - me - nots,
Pur - ple cro - cus - es, pur - ple cro - cus - es,
Gold - en but - ter - cups, gold - en but - ter - cups,

sway - ing to and fro. _____ A
sway - ing to and fro. _____ A
sway - ing to and fro. _____ A
sway - ing to and fro. _____ A

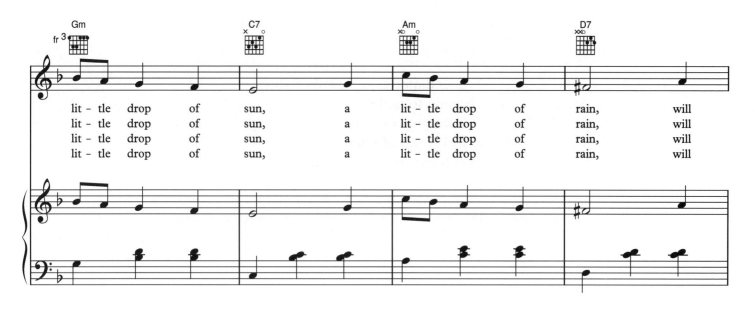

lit – tle drop of sun, a lit – tle drop of rain, will
lit – tle drop of sun, a lit – tle drop of rain, will
lit – tle drop of sun, a lit – tle drop of rain, will
lit – tle drop of sun, a lit – tle drop of rain, will

make the daf – fo – dils grow.
make the for – get – me – nots grow.
make the cro – cus – es grow.
make the but – ter – cups

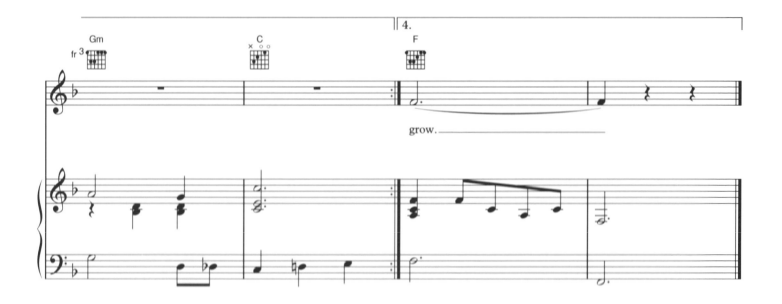

grow.

Yellow daffodils, yellow daffodils
Swaying to and fro
A little drop of sun
A little drop of rain
Will make the daffodils grow

(Further verses could include Blue forget-me-nots; Purple Crocuses;
Sweet, pink roses; Bright red tulips; Yellow buttercups etc etc)

Actions

Yellow daffodils, yellow daffodils *Swaying to and fro*	} }	Sway in time to the music
A little drop of sun	-	Draw a circle in the air
A little drop of rain	-	Hold hands high and move them down whilst wiggling fingers
Will make the daffodils grow	-	Raise hands upwards

Tiny Little Fingernails

Words and Music by
Niki Davies

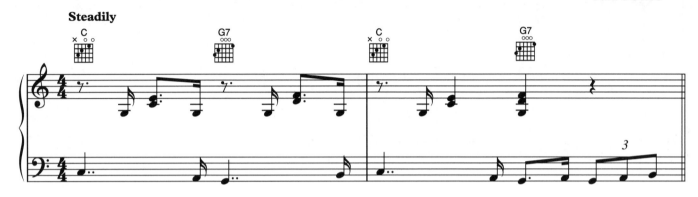

Ti - ny lit - tle fin - ger - nails, ti - ny lit - tle toes, ti - ny lit - tle hands and
Ti - ny lit - tle ears___ and ti - ny lit - tle cheeks, ti - ny lit - tle knees and

ti - ny lit - tle nose: that's how I start - ed out to be___ but
ti - ny lit - tle feet:

now I'm big – ger, just look at me! We are grow – ing as

child – ren do and soon we will be big – ger than you.

big – ger than you.

1. Tiny little fingernails, tiny little toes
   Tiny little hands and tiny little nose
   That's how I started out to be
   But now I'm bigger, just look at me!
   We are growing as children do
   And soon we will be bigger than you!

2. Tiny little ears and tiny little cheeks
   Tiny little knees and tiny little feet
   That's how I started out to be
   But now I'm bigger, just look at me!
   We are growing as children do
   And soon we will be bigger than you!

Actions

Point to the different parts of the body as they are mentioned in the song.

That's how I started out to be	-	Point to self
But now I'm bigger, just look at me!	-	Hold hand above head to suggest being very tall
We are growing as children do	-	Squat down, then rise up to full height with arms held high
And soon we will be bigger than you	-	Point finger at audience (or teacher)

Section Two:
Musical Activity - Sound effects to a poem

The Early Birds Poem

Early in the morning as the sun begins to rise,
Three white doves sing, "coo, coo, coo".
Early in the morning as the sun begins to rise,
Three melodious thrushes sing "chirp, chirp, chirp".
Early in the morning as the sun begins to rise,
Four tiny sparrows sing "twitter, twitter, twitter".
Early in the morning as the sun begins to rise,
Four tuneful cuckoos sing "cuckoo, cuckoo, cuckoo".
Early in the morning as the sun begins to rise,
Five pretty robins sing "cheep, cheep, cheep".
Early in the morning as the sun begins to rise,
Five black crows sing "caw, caw, caw".
Early in the morning as the sun begins to rise,
Six lively blackbirds sing "tweet, tweet, tweet"
They all sing together as the sun begins to rise.
Then, away fly the thrushes,
Away fly the sparrows,
Away fly the cuckoos,
Away fly the robins,
Away fly the crows,
Away fly the blackbirds,
Leaving three white doves to "coo, coo, coo"
Late into the summer afternoon.

Ask the children if they can think of any instruments which might sound like birdsong and collect together a selection of these instruments, ie penny whistles, toy xylophones and glockenspiels, wind chimes etc. Assign each instrument to a particular bird; here are some suggestions:

Doves - Low chime bars
Thrushes - Indian bells
Sparrows - Finger cymbals
Cuckoos - Any tuned percussion instrument playing a repeated E-C
Robins - Small triangles
Crows - Guiros/scrapers
Blackbirds - High chime bars or glockenspiels

You could also get the children to make their own bird instruments. The following are just a few ideas you could develop:

Crow/Raven
Take some corrugated paper and cut into large rectangles (about 30 cm x 15 cm) ensuring the corrugated ridges run horizontally along the shorter edge. Paint the rectangles with bright colours and roll into a long tube secured with sticky tape. Now take a stick or a pencil and run up and down the tube to make a 'caw' sound.

Twittering Birds
Thread a number of milk bottle tops onto a piece of string or cotton. Tie the ends together and use as a shaker.

Melodic Birds
Place some glass bottles in a line (you could use milk bottles). Fill the bottles with water, each to a different level. Now use a tea-spoon (or other metal implement) to draw across the bottles creating a melodic tinkling effect. You could also strike each bottle individually for a cheeping effect.

Divide the children into groups (the size of these will depend on the number of children in the class and the number of bird sounds you have managed to collect). Give each group a bird name and each child the relevant instrument for their bird.

The groups are now ready to add sound effects to the poem. Either read the poem yourself or get a group of older children to read it. As each group of birds begin to sing, the children representing that bird should begin to play their instruments. There will be a natural growth of sound as each new group of birds enters. In the latter part of the poem this sound diminishes as the birds begin to fly away. The children should stop playing as their bird flies away leaving only the doves cooing.

The number of birds in the poem may be reduced or increased according to the number of children and instruments available - or you may wish to make the poem shorter and simpler by using fewer, larger groups, eg eight white doves, eight melodious thrushes, eight tiny sparrows and eight tuneful cuckoos.

<u>Further work with tuned & untuned percussion</u>

The Birdie Band!

As with the Early Birds poem, divide the children into groups of birds and give them instruments to represent their birds. You may decide to have only two or three groups, or more if wished. These groups make up The Birdie Band!

You are the conductor of The Birdie Band and are there to indicate when each group should begin playing and stop playing. To do this you need to develop either hand signals, vocal signals or pictorial signals for each bird which the children will understand and respond to. One idea would be to make picture/flash cards for each bird. The children can help make these by painting a picture of their group's bird or using pictures from magazines. You could also write the name of the bird under the picture to aid word learning and reading.

Sit the children in their groups on the floor and ask them to cross their arms and face you. Explain that when you indicate for their bird to 'sing' they should pick up their instrument and begin to play. When you indicate for their bird to stop 'singing' they should stop playing, put their instrument down and cross their arms again. You may want to make the game harder by introducing two birds at the same time or using signals to direct the band to play softly or loudly (ie arms crossed indicates soft; arms out wide indicates loud).

Section Two:
Music & Movement

Use the backing tracks on the enclosed CD for the children to act and mime out the following (each track is one minute long):

1. **Flower Growing**
   Sit crouched. Make a shoot appear above the ground with your hand. Slowly rise up. Be the stem, the leaves, the head. Grow and grow until you reach your full glory.

2. **Bird Hatching**
   The bird moves a little inside the egg, then moves more and jerks - moves more still and begins to peck at the inside of the shell. Even more movement and pecking, until, at the end of the music, the bird breaks out of the shell.

3. **Shadow** (get the children to work in pairs with a leader and a shadow)
   a. Run on tiptoe.
   b. Move smoothly, slowly and gracefully.
   c. Begin very small, grow enormous, become small again (repeat).
   d. Be sleepy - gradually lie down.

4. **Thunder Clouds**
   Be the clouds, becoming bigger as they move across the sky.
   Be big flashes of lightning (leap into the air).
   Be the thunder (clap hands with body stretched high, then low, then one side, then the other).

5. **Flames**
   Be a tiny, flickering flame which gets bigger and bigger as more flames join it, until you are a roaring fire. Now become smaller and smaller until you are again a tiny, flickering flame.

6. **Sunflower**
   Let your leaves (arms) flap gently in the breeze, first one, then the other. Begin to sway, nod your head, bend one way then the other, etc.

7. **Balloon**
   Begin as small as you can be. Grow gradually, bigger and bigger until you pop! (Leap into the air, arms and legs splayed.)

Section Two:
Curriculum Linked Activities

SCIENCE

1. Grow some plants from seed in the classroom.
2. Examine a few different sizes and shapes of seeds. Look at pictures of the flowers, plants, etc that they could grow into.
3. Match pictures of baby animals and birds with their parents, eg a chick with a chicken.

SCIENCE/ART

1. Look at some sunflower seeds.
   Make a life-size Mister Sunflower for the classroom. The children could paint and cut out large, yellow petals for Mister Sunflower's head.

2. Make a 'Growing' collage for a wall display. Get the children to paint pictures of vegetables, flowers, plants, leaves for a tree, short grass, long grass, a sun, rain clouds, etc. You could even dry some real leaves and flowers and stick these to the collage.

MATHS

Collect together a number of different seeds and get the children to sort these into big, medium and tiny seeds by placing them in appropriately marked dishes.

You could also choose to expand on some of the links that the songs in section one make with the keystage one science curriculum, such as:

Mummy's Tummy's Growing	Humans as organisms
Balloon	Changing materials Forces and motion
Mister Sunflower	Green plants and organisms
Two Birds	Light and sound
Yellow Daffodils	Green plants and organisms

Section Three:
A Musical Episode - The Window Sill

This small musical play takes elements from sections one and two of this book and links them together into a performance that the children, parents and teachers can all enjoy. You can choose to keep theproduction simple whereby all the children will sing every song, with each group of characters standing out from the choir for its part in the play; or you may like to make it more elaborate by using costumes and possibly having some children acting and singing solos from the songs. You may also choose to use other songs from section one and adapt the text in the play accordingly - have fun!

Cast List

Narrator   The teacher or an older child would be ideal for this role.

Alice   The name of this character can be changed to the actual name of any girl or boy chosen to play the part.

Blades of grass   Select some suitably grass-like children for these parts.
                      Suggested Costume: All green attire - e.g. leggings and t-shirt

Alice's Shadow   It's a good idea to choose a child who's slightly smaller than Alice.
                      Suggested Costume: All black attire or similar dress to Alice

Daffodils and other flowers   Select some children who are particularly good at swaying and pretending to grow like a flower. Along with the daffodils, the children can choose other flowers they would like to be.
                      Suggested Costume: Coloured tops with green skirts or trousers. The children could also make large green paper leaves to attach to their arms.

Animals   You'll need children to be a duckling, a puppy, a kitten, a piglet and a chick for these characters.
                      Suggested Costume: The children could make masks to look like their animal - or if you're feeling really adventurous, what about some face painting!

Mister Sunflower Choose one of the taller children in the class for this part.
                      Suggested Costume: A large cardboard circle painted like the head of a sunflower with holes cut for eyes would be particularly effective.

Scenery

The main prop for the play is the window sill. It is important that this can be lowered to a height where Alice can look over easily at the end of the musical. (Why not paint a wall on a large piece of card with a window sill at the top? This can be balanced on boxes at the beginning of the play and the boxes removed for the end. Or you could have a fold at the bottom of the card which turns under to lower the level when necessary.)

Script

Narrator:
Little Miss Alice White
Stood up on her toes
She stretched and stretched up, really high
As high as she could go.

For a while, she tried again,
She tried and tried, but still,
Miss Alice White could not see
Over her window sill.

This made Alice very sad
She wished that she could grow
She often wondered what she could do
And if anyone else would know.

So every day she went for a walk
Down the leafy lane,
But, whoever she met and spoke to
The answers were always the same.

[The blades of grass step forward and Alice walks to meet them.]

Alice:
Grass, grass, growing so fast,
Why can't I grow too?

Blades of grass:
We don't know, we don't know,
We have no answer for you.

SONG:
EACH LITTLE BLADE OF GRASS

[The little shadow comes out from the choir and starts to follow Alice, mimicking every move she makes. They turn to face each other.]

Alice:
Shadow, shadow, growing so fast,
Why can't I grow too?

Shadow:
I don't know, I don't know,
I have no answer for you.

SONG
LITTLE SHADOW *(During the song, Alice and her shadow can mime according to the words.)*

[The flowers step forward.]

Alice:
Flowers, flowers, growing so fast,
Why can't I grow too?

Flowers:
We don't know, we don't know,
We have no answer for you.

SONG:
YELLOW DAFFODILS

[The baby animals step forward.]

Alice: Animals, animals, growing so fast,
Why can't I grow too?

Animals: We don't know, we don't know,
We have no answer for you.

SONG: DUCKLING, DUCKLING, YOU WILL GROW

Narrator: Every day for a year or more
Alice asked the same question until
She thought that she would never
See over her window sill.

But then she met a sunflower
Who waved and nodded his head
Alice asked him "Why can't I grow like you?"
And this is what he said:

Sunflower: You _are_ growing as children will,
Now run home, and look over your window sill.

[Alice runs off stage (or to the back of the choir).]

SONG: MISTER SUNFLOWER
(During the song, alter the window sill to the lower height.)

[Alice re-enters.]

Narrator: Alice looked through her window
She could see the trees and the hills,
And she shouted out as loud as she could:

Alice: I can see over my window sill!

SONG: TINY LITTLE FINGERNAILS

Everything's Growing
by Niki Davies
CD Track Listing

Section One: Songs To Sing (with vocals)
1. Mummy's Tummy's Growing
2. Grandad's Whiskers
3. Each Little Blade Of Grass
4. The Balloon Is Getting Bigger
5. Daddy's In The Garden
6. Little Shadow (Echo Song)
7. Mister Sunflower
8. Duckling, Duckling, You Will Grow
9. Thunder Storm
10. Two Birds, Singing A Song For Me
11. Yellow Daffodils
12. Tiny Little Fingernails

Backing Tracks
13. Mummy's Tummy's Growing
14. Grandad's Whiskers
15. Each Little Blade Of Grass
16. The Balloon Is Getting Bigger
17. Daddy's In The Garden
18. Little Shadow (Echo Song)
19. Mister Sunflower
20. Duckling, Duckling, You Will Grow
21. Thunder Storm
22. Two Birds, Singing A Song For Me
23. Yellow Daffodils
24. Tiny Little Fingernails

Section Two: Music & Movement
25. Flower Growing
26. Bird Hatching
27. Shadow
28. Thunder Clouds
29. Flames
30. Sunflower
31. Balloon

Section Three: The Window Sill
32. Each Little Blade Of Grass (Backing track)
33. Little Shadow (Backing track)
34. Yellow Daffodils (Backing track)
35. Duckling, Duckling, You Will Grow (Backing track)
36. Mister Sunflower (Backing track)
37. Tiny Little Fingernails (Backing track)

In certain instances the arrangements on the recording may differ to those inside the book.

Reproduced and printed by
Halstan & Co. Ltd., Amersham, Bucks., England